The Big Hunger

to Catherine,
this is it !
Linda Giles

The Big Hunger

Five Foundations for a Healthier You

Linda Giles

Life Inspired Publications
Honolulu

Order this book online at www.trafford.com/07-3028
or email orders@trafford.com

Most Trafford titles are also available at major online book retailers.

Published by Life Inspired Publications, Honolulu, Hawaii

Cover art and illustrations by Sarah Corry.

Note for Librarians: A cataloguing record for this book is available from Library and Archives Canada at www.collectionscanada.ca/amicus/index-e.html

Printed in Victoria, BC, Canada.

ISBN: 978-1-4251-6550-5

We at Trafford believe that it is the responsibility of us all, as both individuals and corporations, to make choices that are environmentally and socially sound. You, in turn, are supporting this responsible conduct each time you purchase a Trafford book, or make use of our publishing services. To find out how you are helping, please visit www.trafford.com/responsiblepublishing.html

Our mission is to efficiently provide the world's finest, most comprehensive book publishing service, enabling every author to experience success. To find out how to publish your book, your way, and have it available worldwide, visit us online at www.trafford.com/10510

www.trafford.com

North America & international
toll-free: 1 888 232 4444 (USA & Canada)
phone: 250 383 6864 ♦ fax: 250 383 6804
email: info@trafford.com

The United Kingdom & Europe
phone: +44 (0)1865 722 113 ♦ local rate: 0845 230 9601
facsimile: +44 (0)1865 722 868 ♦ email: info.uk@trafford.com

10 9 8 7 6 5 4 3 2

For Kelly …
During every moment of every day
for the past seventeen years
I have felt blessed beyond measure
to call you my husband.

Contents

Acknowledgements

I want to acknowledge all those that I have been privileged to walk part of this journey with. I have been inspired by and grateful for each and every person who took part in a Five Foundations class. I have learned more from all of you than you have learned from me.

To my editor, Matt, for your steady nature and your beautiful gift of editing; for taking my writing and making it the book I dreamed it could be. Your patience and belief in what I had to share was exactly what I needed.

To Sarah, for the illustrations of the labyrinth on the cover and within these pages, thank you for being open and willing to create exactly what I had pictured.

To all the loving, caring people who never lost faith in the fact that this book would be completed. First and foremost, Kathy, who told me again and again and again that it would be perfect and exactly what it needed to be and to listen to my heart and be true to only that. I can't imagine my life without you, and thank goodness I don't have to. To Kate, my biggest fan and supporter—or my PR manager, as she calls herself. Your presence in my life is meant to be and I'm keeping you forever. To Donna, who knew what I had inside me even before I did and baby-stepped me all the way to the doors of Unity, where I felt like I had come home. To Mary, for once-a-month coffee sessions that over the years became more and more important—your unconditional love and friendship is a gift. To Susan, who edited the beginnings of this book years ago and has been my friend, mentor, and supporter ever since. To Toby, who continues to amaze and motivate me with her dreams and ingenuity. I'll never forget our meetings to keep each other on track at "our office" —the food court at Ala Moana.

To my parents, who pushed me to reach my potential and expected the best from me. You helped me expect that from myself. Thank you, Dad, for my strength and Mom, for my kindness—two things I would not be me without.

To my children, Keegan and Olivia Kate, who bring a smile to my face every day. You have both been patient and loving as I have learned to be a working mom, with the emphasis on mom. I cherish our time together.

And finally, to my sweet husband Kelly. This book began with the fairy tale of meeting you. Your unconditional love continues to be the best part of my life. I am not sure how I was lucky enough to be on the receiving end of your affection, kindness and dedication, but I am grateful every day.

The labyrinth is a spiritual symbol that has been around for about 3,500 years. A labyrinth is not a maze; there are no tricks or dead ends in the path. There is a single winding path from the edge to the center.

A labyrinth is a walking meditation device. It represents the journey inward to our true selves. There is one way in and one way out of a labyrinth, but there is no wrong way. Any way you choose to walk a labyrinth is the right way for you. As you walk the journey through the Five Foundations, you will discover there is only one way that will allow you to truly become a healthier person—and that is *your* way. Enjoy the walk.

INTRODUCTION

"Getting started, keeping going, getting started again—
in art and in life, it seems to me
this is the essential rhythm ..."
—Seamus Heaney

In today's world we have experts in every area of life ready to tell us what to do, ready to tell us it's possible and that we can do it. I know this is true with weight loss. I did what other people told me to do and I succeeded—for a while. Once the cheering stopped and I stopped doing exactly what the experts said, I felt like I had failed and the journey was over.

The problem is that we look to the experts to tell us what is best for us. But they don't know. No matter how wonderful they are, they are not you, and they are not the expert on you. I lost 75 pounds and have kept it off for fifteen years—that has been a journey. Having done that, some people have looked to me as an expert. If an expert means someone who has all the answers, then I am not an expert.

Though I am not an expert, I have an intense desire to share some basic things that are paramount to the journey of losing weight and getting healthier. I have discovered so much on my journey and want others to know that they can accept themselves, trust themselves, and most importantly, be kind to themselves.

Acceptance, trust, and kindness are central themes in The Big Hunger and are the basis of what I call the "Five Foundations." As outlined in this book, the Five Foundations can be applied to anyone's life. They are not meant to be hard and fast rules. They are meant to be molded and used to fit into the only life you are living—yours.

A wise friend told me that a book is never truly done. As I have spent years talking about, reflecting about, teaching about and writing about the Five Foundations, I have realized the absolute truth of what my friend told me. This book has been a journey, taken one step at a time, like any other journey. The journey to lose weight, the journey to build something, the journey to become the person you want to be—none of these things happens overnight, and neither did this book.

In every journey there are days when you want to give up, days when you are embarrassed at what little progress you have made, days when you doubt that you can do it, days when the reasons you started the journey seem meaningless, days when you just want to cry, days when you feel smothered and overwhelmed. I experienced all these and more. Thankfully, the journey of writing this book not only brought all these experiences into my life, it also brought angels. In fact, it brought many angels into my life, without whom this book would not have been published.

We all need support, encouragement and understanding. I am fortunate to have experienced these things throughout every important journey of my life. I truly believe we must surround ourselves with those who lift us up: those people who leave us feeling better once we spend time with them; those who bring out the best in us. My life is full of people who do this every day.

But here's the thing: The person sitting in your seat is the only one who can actually take the action necessary to make progress. You can have a million people telling you that you can do it. A million people cheering you on. A million people expecting you to succeed. And yet, you are the only one who can do it.

We are all on a journey, and the only way to truly succeed is to keep going. On the days when you agonize, the days you want to quit, the days you can't remember why you even started, it is even more important to take just one more step. That is how this book was written. That is how I got to a weight I feel great about. And that is how

I am living a life I love—one day at a time, one action at a time, one thought at a time.

If I can do it, so can you. I promise.

THE CHOICE IS YOURS

I see so many people who are miserable, exhausted and sad, who are struggling with food and weight issues. But the real problem is not food or weight. The problem is about finding yourself and the life you want to live. It's about excavating who you are, discovering and sometimes even inventing that person—and honoring who that person is.

Every person I see struggling calls me to action. There is absolutely no need for anyone—for you—to be living a life you don't love. I believe that every person on this earth was born to experience the joy in life. It's there for the making.

As children, our choices are limited. When we become adults, we can choose the way we allow the past to affect us. No matter what your past was like—and for most of us, it was not all roses—it is only your past. It is not your present or your future, nor does it have to determine your present or your future. It's time to learn to let your past be just that, passed!

It is time to take responsibility for your life and all choices you make. So many of us are stuck in the habit of a "regular" day that we can't see any further. Well, today is a new day and it can be different, if you choose. Sometimes we feel something is missing but can't put our finger on what "it" is. Anne Morrow Lindbergh wrote, "In fact, the problem is how to feed the soul." If your "regular" day yesterday didn't feed your soul, then I don't think it will do the trick today either. Doing the same action over and over and expecting a different result is the definition of insanity. We need to change something if we want our life to change.

My guess is that you are reading this book because you want to be happy, you want to be fulfilled, and you want to feel good about yourself. You can have all of those things and more—the choice is yours.

> *"First say to yourself what you would be;*
> *and then do what you have to do."*
> —Epictetus

THE FIVE FOUNDATIONS

1. The Big Hunger: Be Compassionate with Yourself.

2. The Little Hunger: Eat What You Want, When You're Hungry.

3. Hara Hachi Bu*: Live, Eat, and Be in Moderation.

4. Trust Your Body: Stop — Listen — Trust.

5. Food is Fuel: Choose to Eat to Live.

The literal translation from the Japanese is "eight-tenths full."

THE BIG HUNGER

I spent the first twenty-three years of my life as a dieter; swinging back and forth between being "perfect" and being "terrible," back and forth between starving and stuffed. Not once, in all those years, did these diets tell me that the hunger I was unable to satisfy was not coming from my stomach. It was a bigger hunger. It was a hunger for love and friendship and inner peace and wholeness. Food could never give those things to me. But I could give them to myself.

Hunger. It's been a big issue for me. Physical hunger as well as the kind you can't feed. That aching and emptiness you desperately want to fill but don't seem to know how. A hunger for the life you want and the person you want to be. A hunger to have a sense of meaning and purpose. It is your soul crying out to be fulfilled and at peace.

In Africa, they refer to the "big" hunger and the "little" hunger. The little hunger is the hunger of our stomach; the need to put nourishment in our bodies to survive. The big hunger is much deeper: it is a hunger for acceptance, completion, and meaning.

As I have tried to come up with a succinct way of describing the big hunger, I have realized it is different for everyone. Just like the little hunger is fulfilled with different things and in different ways for each individual, so is the big hunger.

For many, the big hunger includes a need for connection with other human beings. For me, when I met my husband and he loved me completely—in a way I had never been loved—a huge part of my big hunger was fulfilled. As I made my way through jobs that seemed to be right for me, but left me hungry, I created my own business, called Life Inspired. Life Inspired allows me to connect with others while also supporting them in positive change.

When people saw me after I had lost weight, they always had one question: How did I do it? Not having spent a lot of time pondering this, I started giving the answer that seemed true to me. "I got happy." It was true. I got happy, and food was not as important anymore. As I gave this answer and watched the differing reactions, most were not positive. "You mean, I have to get happy? Well, with the life I'm living now, that's not gonna happen." Or, "That's a pretty tall order—get happy? Really?" Then once, after a nasty confrontation at a Christmas Eve party, someone who had consumed a few stiff drinks sputtered in my face, "Well, that's such a nice answer. And for those of us who can't do that, what do we do?"

I was tired of being confronted and second-guessed and defensive about how I had changed my life. So I decided to get more specific and tell them exactly what I was doing. That way, anyone could do it—whether they were happy or not. I came up with "I eat what I want when I'm hungry." I was pleased with my new answer, but the people I told weren't. "You mean to tell me you can eat everything you want and look like you do? You make me sick. I hate people who can eat and eat and eat and not gain weight." Or, "You have to pay attention to your body to know when it's hungry? Forget it."

No one liked my answers very much because I was not giving them a quick fix, sure-fire, guaranteed silver bullet that would allow them to lose weight easily. So I stopped telling people the truth.

I started to tell them it was just sensible eating, paying attention, and exercise—and those things did help me get healthier. BUT—and this is a big but—the true answer was that I finally fed the big hunger. I decided to be compassionate with myself and find out what I really longed for.

My life had been a downward spiral, and it frightens me to think back on the direction I was heading. I have no idea of where I would be today if I had not met Kelly. My Kelly. In a very short period of time, my entire life changed and the spiral started heading in the upward direction. He loved me; unconditionally, irreversibly, completely. He loved every part of me.

That love was the sweetest thing I had ever experienced. It had all the excitement of new love but went deeper than that. To a place in me that had never been touched.

I started to love and respect my body. I started to think I was smart. I started to think I was special. I started to tell myself that everything I had been through up to meeting Kelly would allow me to truly appreciate him. Every terrible thing I thought about myself and did to myself and said to myself had been the best I could do up to that point. I started the process of trying to be a better person. I had wanted to be a different person, but I was trying to fill myself up with food and drink to feel fulfilled. And that simply didn't work.

What did work was feeding the big hunger and being compassionate with myself.

> *"There is more hunger in the world*
> *for love and appreciation than for bread."*
> —Mother Teresa

WE ARE ALL UNIQUE

The big hunger is different for each person. And, like everything in life, the big hunger can change in an instant.

A friend of mine had a stroke two months ago. Before the stroke, purchasing a red couch and painting her walls Tiffany blue was feeding her big hunger. Now, something entirely different will feed it: Being able to feel independent again, spending precious time with a good friend, laughing at what we used to think was important, knowing she is doing the very best she can with her recovery.

To me, life is not worth living if we can't feed the big hunger. Some parts of that hunger may take years to fill; others may require only three minutes, and then it's a new day and we get to fill it all over again.

Just like the little hunger in our stomach, the big hunger cannot be filled just once. It is a day in, day out feeding.

"Everything changes,
nothing remains without change."
—Buddha

THIS IS IT

Seventeen years ago, I made two promises to myself. Those promises altered the course of my life: They allowed me to create a life I love and become the person I am today, a person of whom I am very proud. Every morning I recommit to those promises—and the promise of a new day.

"THIS IS IT!" I say it every day, and I mean it with all my heart. We get each day once—only once—and the uniqueness of each moment calls for very strong promises—followed by action.

Three years ago, I quit my full-time job and told the whole world, "I'm writing a book!" Well, maybe not the whole world, but I did tell at least a few hundred people; it felt like the whole world.

"THIS IS IT!" It was time to follow my passion. And as I sat at my new desk with my new laptop looking out at my backyard, I felt a sense of panic mixed with excitement.

"THIS IS IT!" I had—and still have—an overwhelming sense that anything is possible. I have room to breathe, space to think, and time for *me*. I am in charge of my life and my feelings ... anything is possible.

So, who am I? Why did I want to write this book, and what were these two promises? Let's go back to the beginning, the very beginning.

I was born a BIG girl. My very first trip to the scales, I weighed in at nine-and-a-half pounds, and I entered the world screaming. I was big in size, big in voice and big in personality. While I was learning to walk, lumbering down the sidewalk, my nickname was "the tank"—because I was as wide as I was tall.

When I was three years old, my mother wrote in my baby book: "She is bossy, overaggressive and takes over everything." When I was in kindergarten, she wrote, "wants to read everything, not too good with numbers." On my kindergarten report card the teacher wrote, "talks too much, but is very happy and so excited about school." Yes, I was big in size, big in voice, and big in personality.

It continued this way throughout my whole early life. I was called a big girl. I had big bones, broad shoulders … I was just big. I was given that identity and I fulfilled it. And, like everything I did, I did it to the extreme: I went from plump to chubby to overweight to obese. I was handed an identity, and everyone expected me to live up to that identity. And, frankly, I did too.

Let's fast-forward to after I had graduated from college. I had just finished my student teaching and had returned to my home in Hawaii as a 215-pound, big girl. And that's where I was when I made those two life-transforming promises to myself. Amazing—what was true of me in kindergarten is still true of me—almost. I am big in voice, big in personality—but I am no longer big in size.

Today I am 75 pounds less than when I made those two promises.

*"The great thing in the world
is not so much where we stand,
as in what direction we are moving."*
—Oliver Wendell Holmes

THE TWO PROMISES

Promise number one: I will never diet again. Dieting is what got me to my highest-ever weight of 215 pounds.

To me, dieting is about deprivation. It's about not eating the things you want—which, of course, makes you want them even more. If it is a food or beverage you love, then it is definitely not allowed on a diet. Diets have a beginning and an end. The end signals the end of deprivation, but it also signals the return of all those pounds that were lost—and they usually come back accompanied by "friends." Everyone who has dieted has their own story. My story: lose fifty, gain seventy; lose seventy, gain eighty.

Promise number two: I will listen to and trust my body. Beginning in childhood, we get mixed signals about our bodies. Here's how it was for me: If I was still hungry after a meal, and if I let someone know I was hungry, I was usually admonished with, "You can't be hungry!"

"Okay," I would think to myself. "I thought this feeling in my stomach meant I was hungry, but I must be wrong."

Or this classic dinner table scene: "I'm full, I'm done." And an adult says, "Just three more bites." Okay. So now I feel full but someone is telling me to eat more.

Or, "Clean your plate. There are starving children in _____." You get to fill in the blank; exactly where in the world varies depending on your age, but we were all given this message! Even as a child I never quite understood how eating my peas would help the starving children in the world, but what I did get was the guilty feeling. And so I learned to clean my plate, no matter what I felt inside.

How about this one: "I worked hard to put this food on the table; you'd better eat it and appreciate it whether you are hungry or not." How confusing is this?

And so, with the repetition of these messages over many years, we learned not to trust ourselves, our bodies. Over time, we turned the true hunger switch off—it didn't seem to be working very well or serving any purpose anyway.

With the switch turned off, we would eat for a whole variety of non-hunger reasons. We eat because the food is there, because it smells good, or because someone made it just for us. We eat because it's time, because we feel guilty, because we want to celebrate with our friends, and for many other reasons.

That was true for me. For many years, I never felt true hunger. I would eat in anticipation of hunger. I would notice the time and realize that in a while I was probably going to be hungry soon and I might not be able to get any food then, so I would eat in anticipation of hunger that would come later. I didn't listen and I didn't trust, but I promised myself I would learn how to do this with my body.

> *"Dwell in possibility."*
> —Emily Dickinson

WHAT WERE WE TAUGHT?

We were taught about hunger, and we learned what we were taught. But here's something important we were not taught: We were not taught to trust our bodies. We were not taught to listen to our bodies. We were not taught to respect who we truly are and what we truly want. We were not taught the importance of compassion for ourselves. But just as we were taught all of those things that have not worked well for us, we can teach ourselves to trust and listen to our bodies. We can learn how to respect and have compassion for ourselves.

It is time to learn.

Seventeen years ago, I met a man who helped me start learning that food "fills the hole" and that's all. It doesn't bring you love, it doesn't bring you joy, it doesn't bring you a feeling of fulfillment. It fills the physical hole called your stomach. It provides the nutrition your body needs, *and that is all it does.* Food is fuel.

This man also taught me that I could trust my body, and that if I really tried I would be able to listen again to what I truly wanted and needed.

But the biggest gift this man gave me was that of unconditional love. I had been told many times I was a strong person, a smart person, a beautiful person—and each compliment was always followed with a "but."

"You are a strong person, but you are could try harder."

"You are a smart person, but you need to do it my way."

And my all time favorite, the pretty-face line: "You have such a pretty face, but if you just lost some weight ..."

When I met Kelly, I kept waiting for the "but" clause. When, I wondered, is he going to mention that I'm great "but" he wants me to change something? When is he going to tell me I'm good enough now, "but" there are some things wrong with me? When is the "but" going to come out? Well, it never did, so I married Kelly. I knew a keeper when I saw one. And that "but" has never surfaced in our seventeen years of marriage!

THE FAIRY TALE

One day a girl met a boy. She was a BIG girl with a BIG voice. The boy told the girl she was beautiful and strong and smart. He meant it.

Slowly, she began to believe him.

Other people had told the girl before, but it was always followed with a "but":

"You are beautiful, but if you lost some weight …"

"You are strong, but do what I say …"

"You are smart, but you need to try harder …"

This was different. It was like the boy was holding a mirror for her, reflecting back all the wonderful things he saw so the girl could see them, too.

Every day, he would hold up the mirror, and every day, she began to feel better about herself. She was feeling beautiful and strong and smart.

The boy was from a faraway country and was only visiting. One day he had to go home. He told the girl he would come back.

When he left, the girl was sad—but the boy left her mirror.

The girl showed the mirror to some other people, but the reflection was not the same.

She realized she needed to be very careful with her mirror, because it was hard not to believe everything that was reflected.

She decided she was the best person to hold her mirror.

The boy came back from the faraway country, and the BIG girl with the BIG voice was becoming a small girl with a BIG voice. For the first time in the girl's life, the outside of her was beginning to match the inside of her, and it was good.

Sometimes the girl gave the mirror to the boy and sometimes she kept it.

She was beautiful and strong and smart—her mirror told her so.

THE MIRROR

Who's holding *your* mirror? You *do* have a mirror, and *somebody* is holding it right now. It might be you, it might be someone else, or it could even be a whole assortment of people and it probably changes throughout the day.

We *all* have a mirror that we look into every single day.

Most mirrors reflect what is on the outside of a person, but the mirror I am talking about is different.

Yes, it does reflect what we look like, but it also tells us what we are like on the inside.

Your ideas—about who you are, what is important, and the value you place on who you are—are all reflected in that mirror. Yes, it shows you whether you are short or tall, heavy or slim, have brown hair or blue eyes, a cute nose or a regal one, but it also tells you what those physical attributes *mean*.

Are you a good person? A capable one? Are you strong, smart, honest? All of that and much, much more, taken together, tells you what kind of a person you are. The mirror also reflects your incredible worth.

When I fell in love, my relationship with everyone changed. Most importantly, my relationship with myself changed. I was suddenly worth taking care of.

THE KEY IS KINDNESS

In dealing with others—especially a small child—it is normal to be compassionate. If a small child is hurt or upset, most people would not react by kicking the child. Most people would hug, comfort, and treat the child gently and lovingly.

You were that small child once. We were all that small child once. You are that child now. We are all that child now. Things do not always go the way we had planned or hoped. We make mistakes and feel terrible about it. When we feel crushed, defeated, hopeless, we need compassion—just like a small child does.

We would give compassion to a hurting child and we need to give it to ourselves.

As I was sitting at an airport waiting to board a plane, I saw a sweet young boy patiently sitting in his car seat. His soulful brown eyes caught mine, and we shared a smile. With a pang in my heart, I remembered when my children were young and innocent and needed car seats. As the airlines called for those traveling with young children, the mother yanked the boy into her arms and grabbed the car seat and headed for the line. I winced at the roughness and hoped and prayed that there were also gentler moments shared between this mother and son.

It is almost unbearable for me to think of children being hurt or sick or abandoned. The innocence and lack of choice on their part feels so unfair. I know that children are hurt and that the world is not fair, but I also know that things can change, and that I can create gentle, tender moments for the children in my life.

Children respond to kindness. So do adults. For example, I go out of my way to take care of an issue with someone who has treated me with kindness. When people are polite, respectful and kind I will make sure they end up happy and taken care of. When someone is mean, hurtful and rude, it is hard to find that place of kindness within myself.

In all my years of working with people I have never once had someone say to me, "Linda, I wasn't doing very well, but then I gave myself a stiff talking to and beat the heck out of myself and now I'm doing great!" What I have heard is, "Now that I am being more gentle and understanding with myself, things are turning around."

It is almost unbearable for me to think of adults being hurt or sick or abandoned. With adults there is a choice. Choosing to kick themselves when they are down—that is a tragedy. Choosing to make things worse with food, alcohol, and drugs does not help. Punishing themselves for being in a terrible situation does not help.

What does help? Kindness, kindness, and more kindness for ourselves. The answer lies in feeding the big hunger, being as compassionate as you can with yourself because you are doing the very best you can with what you have.

> *"Three things in life are important. The first*
> *is to be kind, the second is to be kind,*
> *and the third is to be kind."*
> —Henry James

OUR GIFTS

Acceptance is key to a happy life, yet we seem programmed to be forever dissatisfied. We even reject ourselves. I see it played out over and over, every day.

I grew up all over the world. My father served in the U.S. Army for more than twenty-five years. I realized after many moves with new schools and new teachers and new children and new neighbors that basically I could reinvent myself with every move. No matter how much I didn't like myself in one town, I was sure that the next one would be better. It would always be better in the next place. Does this sound familiar? The grass is always greener, we always want what we don't have, we want to move on because it will be better anywhere else.

Here's a move that will make a difference: It is time to move past this type of thinking.

My mother called me Sarah Bernhardt, and I call my daughter the same because we both have a flair for the dramatic. We are both passionate about everything we believe. We can't help but be that way. That's our true gift, and though others may describe us as "too dramatic," or "too flamboyant," I know—and so does my daughter—that is who we are. I accept those things about me and use those skills every day as a speaker and motivator.

Everyone is born with gifts to share with the world. Sometimes these gifts are exposed from the start and sometimes they need some discovery, nurturing, and attention. Sometimes we view gifts as negative, because that's what someone told us they were.

Like my voice. My voice has been deep and loud from the beginning. Even when I strain to be quiet, it sounds loud. Growing up I was reprimanded and shushed more times than you would think possible. My teachers dutifully noted on my report cards that I talked too much in class. My mother was constantly saying "Shhhh" and holding her finger up to her mouth. "Quiet down, Linda," was her constant refrain. The more excited I was about something the louder I got. I couldn't contain myself.

Today, one of the most common compliments I receive as a speaker is that I have great energy and passion about everything I say. The message I got growing up was that loud is bad; being soft-spoken would be good. I could no more be soft-spoken than I could be an accountant. (My mother wrote in my baby book: "Not so good with numbers" … and it's still not my gift!)

Now that I have accepted my voice, it is my tool. It is my gift. I am proud of my voice and use it to help others.

I think it's great when people find me in a store and say, "I knew you were here. I heard you laughing and talking … I had to come find you." Before I accepted my voice I would have felt shame and embarrassment and would have thought, "Why can't I be more quiet? What is wrong with me? I was so loud someone heard me from the other side of the store!" Now I laugh and think, "I wouldn't have gotten to see this person if they hadn't heard me."

Fault or gift? It's a matter of choice. I'm a talker, and that's what I was put here for. I am convinced that it is my best gift. After most of my speaking engagements, someone lets me know they appreciated what I had to say. I'm a talker—a loud talker. That's who I am, and it's a good thing, and I accept it wholeheartedly.

> *"Make the most of yourself*
> *for that is all there is of you."*
> —Ralph Waldo Emerson

THE ACCEPTANCE OF YOU

Living in a country where struggling and striving are viewed as positive things, it is difficult to stop and accept ourselves. If we are working on improving ourselves, guess what we are paying attention to? The things we feel need fixing. Somewhere inside of us, there is a little voice that keeps telling us: If we accept who we are, then we are stuck. Accepting your life, your weight, your salary seems to mean giving up—it will never be better.

In part, the little voice tells us this because we believe there is a perfect weight, a perfect spouse, a perfect job, and a perfect house—but there isn't. Why? Because the only thing you can definitely count on for the rest of your life is *change*. Change in lifestyle, change in loved ones, change in weight, change in attitudes.

The sad thing is that if we keep waiting for everything to be perfect, we will be sorely disappointed. And then of course we will ask, "What's wrong with me, why can't I get it together?" and blame ourselves. I once read a quote by Marilyn Grey that shows how unrealistic this feat is: "No one ever has it all together. That's like trying to eat once and for all."

True happiness comes from not only accepting but also embracing who you are and where you are in your journey. You *are* who you are, and you *are* where you are. Accepting both of these will open the door for you to have a more fulfilling and satisfying life.

Acceptance does not necessarily mean you love who you are and where you are, but it does mean you are being honest and real with yourself. It means you are open to experiencing more gratitude for where you are along this journey called life.

Accept the wonderful, amazing human being you are. There is only one *you* in the whole world. If you are not true to yourself, the world loses the special things only you can bring to it.

Accept that it is time to stay focused on the things that really matter in your life. Most of us are swept away by life—we move from one small task to the next, adding check mark after check mark to our to-do list. But all the while we are leaving out the most important things, like taking care of *you*. We have been going from one to-do list to the next for so long that most of us don't even know what we really want.

What do you *really* want? What are you passionate about? When was the last time you thought, "I love my life!"

Here's another reason that acceptance is the key to change: You are where you are because of the steps you have already taken. Your current lifestyle is supporting your current life—weight, income, attitude—the things you like and the things you don't like. If you want any of that to change, you need to accept where you are and then be free to take steps to move on.

If you decide not to accept where you are or who you are—where does that leave you? How does that feel? I would bet you would feel less, not more, empowered! What is the opposite of acceptance? Denial, rejection, refusal. Is that what you want to do to yourself?

Everyone else can accept you, but unless *you* accept yourself, it doesn't matter. Others can talk or intimidate you into doing something, but unless you really want to do it, it won't feel good and it won't last.

> *"Thinking is like loving and dying.*
> *Each of us must do it for himself."*
> —Josiah Royce

BIG GIRL

I was a big, strong girl. Not many days went by without a reminder of this. "Linda is a big girl." "Oh, Linda you're just a big girl." "It's just the way she's built, she's a big girl."

It was just a fact, and I heard it over and over, in every way imaginable. I had two younger brothers whom I beat at arm wrestling and protected from bullies. I was strong. Most sports came naturally to me and though I was overweight, I was in good physical shape and very muscular—BIG. I was big, but I was solid and strong.

Strong could also read: rebellious. My strength in body allowed me to be strong in mind also. In many instances in my life I have had people say, "How did you do that?" All I did was decide I was going to do it, so I did. It was simple to me. You just decide, then you do. I was stubborn and stuck to my guns no matter what. I was strong!

If someone told me they knew what was best for me, I would do the opposite. I believe it's been referred to as "cutting your nose off to spite your face." It was exhausting being a rebel, defying everyone with food. I didn't rebel with my clothing or by getting tattoos or strange body parts pierced. I ate and I ate and I ate.

I felt successful in every area of my life except with food. I believed that if I forced myself to lose weight then I would be happy. I would feel peace of mind. What I finally realized was that it was the rest of my life that was leading me to the food and causing me to have disordered eating. Not the other way around.

I needed to accept that being thin would not make me happy and fulfilled. Being happy and fulfilled would lead to my being thin. Food and disordered eating are pointless when you are receiving what you truly want and need. It's not food—I promise.

A friend of mine loved art and decided to become an art teacher. She taught high school art, and it exhausted her. She would come home after school and take a two-hour nap, every day. She didn't feel fulfilled or happy. So, she went to graduate school and became a lawyer—a very good lawyer. Now, she can pull an all-nighter and still be fresh the next day in court, no nap required.

Wow! I can't think of two less similar jobs. She had been a good teacher, but she is a *great* lawyer. She is passionate about practicing law. It plays to her strengths and it shows.

Deep inside of us, we know who we are; what we need to do is to uncover it. We were all put here for a purpose.

There are no mistakes. After years and years of having others tell us who they think we are, it is time for us to decide and accept who we truly are and build on that. We can accomplish this with our own motivation and the support of those in our lives who are "builders."

In the end, it doesn't matter what anyone else thinks about you. It only matters what you think about yourself. To make up things that are not true and live in denial about who you really are is a painful existence.

Accept that you are a gifted, talented individual with unlimited potential.

> *"I celebrate myself, and sing myself."*
> —Walt Whitman

THE POWER OF SELF-TALK

A ccept that you are important enough to take care
of. Taking care of yourself is not, as many people
believe, selfish. In fact, it's just the opposite: Taking care of
yourself allows you to be a blessing in other people's lives.
And the most basic level of how we determine our self-
care, whether we feel "worth it" or not, is by our self-talk,
the way we communicate with ourselves.

Perhaps the most powerful influence on your attitude,
health and well-being is what you say to yourself—the
recording devise that is playing in your head. We all have
one, but many are not aware of what is being recorded.

Self-talk refers to the words and thoughts you use to
describe or evaluate any situation. Self-talk reflects what
you believe about a situation. It is your perception. And
perception is everything; it is your reality, day in and day
out.

There is power in every moment. In one moment, your
conscious mind can hold only one thought at a time—*one*
thought. You get to choose to make your perception of each
moment—your reality—positive or negative. "Hmmm,

this is a problem." Or, "Wow, this is an opportunity." It seems so simple: Just look on the bright side ... the glass is half full. Your response happens in seconds, and if the tape in your head is negative, that's what pops up immediately. Simple, but not always easy.

We are all constantly giving ourselves messages. The mind is an amazing thing; you can be thinking about a number of things in rapid sequence, like what you are doing right now and what you will do later in the day and your to-do list, all within a very short period of time. But along with that focused, conscious thinking, there is another mental activity that is constantly recurring in our minds, and that is our self-talk. We are always reviewing, sometimes criticizing, hopefully praising, our own feelings, choices, and actions. This is the essence of self-talk.

For many people I know (and for myself for many years of my life), most of our self-talk is negative and critical. We may not mean to talk that way to ourselves, but it's an ingrained habit. It's like the tune or words to a familiar song—it just starts playing and keeps on going whether you think about it or not.

Here's both the problem and the potentially positive power of self-talk: *You believe everything you say to yourself.* Everything! That's why it is so important to eliminate as much negative self-talk as possible from our minds.

When you focus on the things you feel good about, it reminds you of your strength and positive qualities. It encourages you to be a little gentler with yourself for the "not so positive." It might even help you realize that the less positive aspects of your life may in fact be your strengths—remember my loud voice!

None of us can say we are perfect, but we can all say we are moving in the right direction. And who wants to be perfect, anyway? Where is there to go from perfect but down? How long can you stay perfect? One day? One week?

I lost 70 pounds in four months once. I had a deadline. I was "commando," running twice a day, surviving on as little food as possible.

One week after the event I lost weight for, I had already gained five pounds back. My immediate thought was, "I wonder how long it's going to take for it to all come back." I told myself that since I gained a little back, it was all over and it was all coming back. Well, it took five months, and it brought friends.

Such is the power of self-talk.

> *"We are shaped by our thoughts;*
> *we become what we think."*
> —Buddha

THE MESSAGES

The bottom line about self-talk is this: It's your choice! It's your mind. If you choose to put in a positive thought, that's what you dwell on; if you choose a negative thought, then that's what you dwell on.

In the first session of my Five Foundations class people share a little about themselves and their relationship with food and their body. Here are some of the things that have been shared:

I hate my body.

I need help desperately.

I hate myself.

Food takes care of me.

I'm confused.

Food has always been my solace, my comfort, my companion.

I eat for every reason there is, except the right one, which, of course, is to live.

If these are the kind of messages we are giving ourselves, there is little doubt about why we struggle with our eating and our bodies. Every time you catch yourself thinking something negative, say "… until now." The more we reinforce negative feelings and thoughts, the more deeply we believe them. We need to tell ourselves that no matter how long we have had a particular problem, it lasted only *until now*.

At this very moment, you have a choice. You can think about whatever you want. It can be a thought that moves you forward and makes you feel good and empowered and better than you've felt in a long time, or it can be a thought that holds you back and makes you feel bad about yourself and takes you further from your goal. It's your choice. The past has no power over you. This is a new moment. Your moment. Be the person you want to be. And remember, there is no wrong way to be.

It seems much more acceptable to talk negatively about ourselves than to give ourselves a compliment. For example, if I met you for lunch and said, "I am having such a bad hair day," you might say, "No, it doesn't look that bad," or "Oh, we all have those days," or you might just smile sympathetically. You probably wouldn't think it odd that I criticized my hair.

If, on the other hand, I showed up and said, "I am so excited! Doesn't my hair look great? It's just the way I love it!" you would probably look at the ground nervously and think, "Okaaay … what's up with Linda?"

Why? There are lots of reasons. What really matters is what we choose to think and speak from here. We have a choice.

> *"The ancestor of any action*
> *is a thought."*
> —Ralph Waldo Emerson

DECIDE

Julia recently shared with me that each evening as she drifts off to sleep she concentrates on what she wants to put energy into. She finds it helps her to have a focus in her life.

Right now she is focusing on learning to talk nicely to herself about her body. Her goal is to actually start to appreciate all the amazing things her body does for her and to nurture it. So instead of bashing her dimpled thighs and wide feet, she is grateful and appreciative and loving, because those thighs and feet are the only ones she has, and they help her accomplish many things, and they deserve to be nurtured.

Another woman told me she has decided to end forty-four years of negative self-talk. Someone asked how she was going to do that. She simply replied, "I *decided*. Once I realized that beating myself up was not helping me, and once I got clear about how ridiculous it was, I stopped."

The root of the word decide is "cide," which means to "kill off." Pesticide is to kill off pests, and homicide is to kill a human being. To decide means to kill off all other options.

Only you can make decisions for you. Decide.

"Once you make a decision,
the universe conspires to make it happen."
—Ralph Waldo Emerson

AWARENESS

One day Jennifer told me dejectedly, "I will never lose weight." Well, there you have it. What you say is what you believe, and what you believe is what you will do.

When Jennifer told me she would never lose weight, I asked her, "Is that true? Will you never lose weight?"

"Is that true?" is a good question to ask yourself when you engage in negative self-talk. Usually your answer will be, "You know, it's not true—I could lose weight!"

But that wasn't the case for Jennifer. Instead, she looked me straight in the eye and answered, "Yes."

I asked why she was so sure. She told me because she wasn't worth it. I begged to differ. Here was an amazingly smart, funny, kind, giving, and successful woman.

I asked her to say out loud, "I am worth it."

She looked at her lap and started to cry. I gently asked her again, "Can you say it?"

She shook her head to indicate no. I asked if she could say it to herself, in her head. Again, unable to speak, she gestured no. Lastly I asked her if she could write it down. Still unable to use words, she indicated a negative response.

As a child she was given messages that she should come last. She learned her lessons well and carried them into adulthood: As a wife, her husband was more important; as a mother, her children were more important. Everyone else came first, so she had no worth. She didn't deserve it. So, as an adult, she could not yet express, "I am worth it."

No matter what you have been told or made to feel, you are worth it. You deserve to know your worth. You are not a victim. You get to choose what you say to yourself day in and day out. It changes your whole life when you start saying more empowering, positive, optimistic things to yourself.

Asking, "Is that true?" is not an instant solution. It takes practice and time to change negative self-talk to empowering self-talk. Remember, many of those negative messages have been with us since childhood, which may mean years, even decades, of repeating the same limiting message, over and over again. First gain awareness, then focus on making the change. Always have patience with yourself, and remember that you are on a journey.

"Nurture your mind with great thoughts."
—Benjamin Disraeli

THE TEACHER

When I started my teaching career, I took the first job I was offered. In my job interview, they asked me how I felt about at-risk youth. I replied that I wanted to motivate and inspire students, and that at-risk youth probably needed me the most. I was telling the truth, but I had no idea what I was getting myself into.

I became part of a school-within-a-school. The philosophy was "arts-based education," and it was excellent. Four core subject teachers would keep the students all four years of high school. We would tie the curriculum together thematically. So, if we were reading *The Diary of Anne Frank* in English class, they were studying World War II in Social Studies, using statistics from this time period in math, etc. This way, the students didn't walk from one class to the other and wipe the slate clean to learn something completely unrelated.

I entered the scene halfway through the first year of the project, and the one hundred and fifty participating students had gone through four English teachers in five months. I was so excited for my first day of being a real teacher. I had no idea what I was teaching that day, but I was ready. The head of the project took me to my classroom, introduced me to the students, and then left.

Okay, what now?

As I looked around at the students, I was shocked to see them eating, drinking, chewing gum, playing cards and completely ignoring me. I explained that I wanted them to get their desks into a semblance of order and get rid of the food, drinks and gum. One young man, Danny, told me they were *allowed* to do all the things they were doing. They made the rules; that's how the project worked. I explained that I agreed in coming up with rules together, but I had not been present for the "rule-making" session at the beginning of the year, so we would do it again—together.

He then shared that I was the fifth English teacher they had had this year and that I was never going to make it through the year. "Two weeks and you're out of here. Two weeks, tops."

Needless to say, this was not the wonderful first day I had in mind, and it was still only first period! Well, quitting was not an option for me, so it was easy for me to tell them I needed this job and was staying. This didn't go over well with Danny. He picked up his desk, yelled "F— you," and threw the desk at me. As he stormed out of the room to go find the head of the project, Danny was yelling, "I'm getting you fired today."

Fast-forward a few months. By being strict, fair and fun, I had built positive relationships with most of my students, even Danny. The students *wanted* to be in my classroom before school, during lunch, and after school. I bought a carpet remnant and set up a reading corner with beanbags and shelves and shelves of books. I listened to the students' problems (the reasons they were at risk) and did my best to be a positive influence. I called parents or guardians regularly to share successes and to ask for help when I needed their support.

I pushed the kids to reach their potential, even though they had horrific things going on at home. If I saw potential in a student, I did my best to bring it out. We did a lot of writing exercises to work through the baggage these young people were already carrying. My classroom was a safe place. It was like home to some of the kids. I was proud every day of the "light bulbs" going on as the students gained insight and awareness. I noted their smiles when they were proud of themselves and of each other. I learned much more from them than they learned from me.

Over a school break, I got a call from the school that my classroom had been vandalized. I couldn't believe it. *Who* would do something like that? *Why* would someone do that? One thing I knew for sure: It could never have been one of my students.

After making an initial visit to the classroom, I decided to leave the room untouched so the students could see the disaster and learn something from it. I believe there is always a lesson to be learned. When break was over, the students came back to school and could not believe what had happened. Graffiti covered the walls, the desks, the rug and the books. My family pictures had been mutilated and hung on the blackboard. All of our beautiful work was destroyed in some way. I could not help but cry along with my students.

We spent the next two days painting and cleaning and putting "our" classroom back together. All the boys kept telling me they were going to find out who did it and "get them." The girls just kept shaking their heads. We all felt violated by someone outside of the project.

A few weeks later, a police officer came to my classroom to inform me that the culprit was in the principal's office. The students in my classroom were so excited, they started hooting and hollering. I walked into the principal's office ready to scream at the mean, terrible, stranger who was responsible for the vandalism.

And there he was. Instead of a stranger, it was the smallest, quietest student in our class, a boy who never talked, but who, I could tell from his writing, was very bright. I had spent a lot of time on the phone with him and his grandmother. I had spent a lot of time in class prodding him to work to his potential. My mouth dropped open. Tears sprang to my eyes. All I could say was, "Why?"

He looked at me slowly, with the hollow eyes I saw every day, and said, "You care too much. Why don't you just leave me alone?"

I was a lone voice for many of my students, a voice that actually told them they were good people, that they had potential, that they should believe in themselves. And for one of them, it was too much.

Did I quit teaching? No? My purpose in life is to teach. From the time I could talk, I was trying to teach everyone something. Every game I played with my brothers or friends I was the teacher or the librarian. I will teach forever. What I teach, and whom I teach, may change, but three things will never change. First, the fact that I am a teacher; second, the way I teach—true learning happens by building relationships, not programs; and third, I will look for and find potential in every person, even if they're not ready to see it themselves.

> *"Nothing is impossible to a willing heart."*
> —John Heywood

SUPPORT

When you have positive relationships and support in your life, things seem to go incredibly well. Trina once told me she had been walking with a neighbor at 6:00 a.m., five days a week, for the past six weeks. They were heading into their seventh week of this positive habit, and it felt great. Trina said of her neighbor, "She's wonderful, just wonderful. The other day it had been raining, and she said she was going to bring me an umbrella. Amazing, she's amazing."

This was a win–win situation for Trina and her neighbor, and that is the best thing about support: It is impossible to help someone else and not benefit in some way yourself.

We were not born to be alone. Yet, in today's society we seem to be losing our sense of community and neighborhood as we move behind closed doors and big fences. We find ourselves more and more alone, yet I believe what we need is more togetherness. Why do we need togetherness? Because we need support, and we need a sense of not being alone. Togetherness is one of the keys to well-being. Meaningful living is truly about the people—not the "things"—in your life.

A certain amount of alone time is important, but to get the most out of life, search out others who know you, understand you, and bring out the best in you.

"I love you, not for what you are, but for who
I am when I am with you."
—Elizabeth Barrett Browning

DIET SODA, TWIX, AND ICE CREAM

When I was teaching high school, which was what I had dreamed about doing since I was five years old, I worked incredibly hard to take care of my students. Those efforts left little time for any self-care.

In reality, I felt lonely anywhere outside the classroom. I felt inept as a teacher. I found myself wondering, "Is it supposed to be this hard? Maybe I'm not cut out for this."

Physically, I felt fat and ugly. I would wake up every day and say, "Today I'm going to be good." And here's what "good" meant: I would have a diet soda on the way to school for breakfast and feel so virtuous. At lunch, one of my students always seemed to be selling candy bars for a fundraiser of some sort. I would think about how "good" I had been at breakfast, so one candy bar wouldn't hurt. Twix or Baby Ruth was my choice. The Baby Ruth had nuts (protein, right?) so when I felt extra healthy I would choose that one. I would buy another diet soda from the teacher's lounge and eat the candy bar in about five seconds.

On the way home, I would stop and get a huge diet soda from a convenience store to try and help with the hunger pangs. I would get home from school around 4:00 p.m. just in time to watch Oprah, but first I needed to reward myself for making it through the day eating only a candy bar and diet soda. I would take the elevator to the mini-mart at the bottom of my condominium building, the whole time dreaming about what I would buy. I am a cookie monster, and the best thing to eat with cookies is ice cream. So, that was usually my poison of choice. I would buy a container of ice cream (the size varied depending on how hard my day was) and then the big choice came: which cookies? Oreos were my favorite, but Nutter Butters were a close second. Some days I would spend so long agonizing over which one I wanted that I would end up getting both.

Riding the elevator back up, I would congratulate myself if I made it all the way to my floor without eating any cookies. But once I got there, I couldn't open the door fast enough. I would rush to my favorite chair, turn on Oprah and let the feast begin.

Day after day after day I spent alone in that apartment trying to eat myself happy, all the while asking myself, "What is wrong with me?" I knew that what I was doing wasn't good for me, I knew it was destroying my health and body (not to mention my self-esteem), and yet day after day, again and again, I repeated the same pattern. Of course, I did have my good moments, even then … occasionally I would go a few days eating only vegetables—and as few of them as I could get by on. But I had this nasty habit of passing out when I didn't eat enough.

Now don't get me wrong, I was a good teacher. In fact, I was nominated for "Beginning Teacher of the Year." I threw myself into my work and spent evenings on the phone with parents and students. I loved my job—but hated myself and the rest of my life.

Professionally, I was doing pretty well. But on a personal level, I was on a downward spiral. I have no idea where I would have ended up if I had not met a kind, caring man who taught me to give myself what I truly wanted and needed—which turned out not to be cookies and ice cream.

Through questioning and writing, I came to realize that what I wanted more than anything was a close relationship. Up till that point, I had never learned how to build a true relationship of any kind—friendly or romantic.

So, I started to learn.

I started to ask myself why I ate so much that it left me uncomfortable and feeling ill. I realized that after growing up feeling deprived of the things I loved to eat, and after having lost large amounts of weight twice and gaining it back, I had reached a conclusion that was at the same time very right, and very wrong: I was sure there was not enough food in the world to satisfy me.

I was right, of course, because no matter how much I ate, I was never satisfied, and never would be. This was a fact I knew—even as I did my "cookie monster" thing day after day. Food was not going to touch the places in my life I was trying to fill.

And I also was wrong, because there was enough food to satisfy my body's needs. It's as if no matter what question I was asking at the time, the answer came up, "Food!" So, I had to figure out what my real answers were.

I had spent most of my life telling myself that I didn't deserve what I wanted and needed. All my growing-up years I felt questioned constantly about what I wanted.

"Why do you want it?"

"You don't need that."

"You can't be hungry."

I thought the only reason I was being denied the things I wanted—food or otherwise—was because I didn't deserve them. So, for twenty-three years I learned to say no to the things I really wanted: new clothes, high-calorie food, and fulfilling relationships. When I gave in, it was with food. Then I felt guilty. The guilt led to eating more, which led to more guilt, which led to … you know the cycle. Food is always the easiest answer. It is readily available, it doesn't question you, and it feels so good in the moment.

I had tried to reason with myself so many times. "Linda, you are a smart person, just stop abusing food. You know it's not good for you." Intellectually, I understood my situation, but that never prevented my cycle of binging and starving.

TRUST YOUR BODY

When I began my final weight loss journey seventeen years ago, I *really* wanted chocolate chip cookie dough and frosting. When I found a cookie shop that sold chocolate chip cookie cups with frosting in them, I thought I had died and gone to heaven.

At about that time, I read a book called *When Food is Love,* by Geneen Roth. She said to trust yourself. I thought, "Okay, this is it. There's one other person in this world who believes I can trust my body—here I go."

My fiancé agreed to support me in whatever would make me happy. I told him I would be eating chocolate chip cookie dough for my meals for the rest of my life. So for the next few days, when we sat down to meals, he would eat something he had made and I would eat chocolate chip cookie dough. I would eat each bite slowly. I tried to make each bite the perfect blend of dough and chips and when I felt satisfied, I would put the cookie dough back in the fridge. Next meal, same thing. Every once in a while I wanted cooked chocolate chip cookies, but raw dough satisfied me immensely. Apparently, I felt very deprived of cookie dough!

Pretty soon my body really wanted a salad. So, I had a great salad. Next morning my fiancé wanted pancakes and I thought, "So do I." For weeks and weeks I ate pancakes and waffles, waffles and pancakes. At some point, I got my fill of those as well. They had been "forbidden foods" from previous diets, and so it was wonderful to be able to eat them slowly, in the presence of another person and feel no guilt at all.

People ask me if I had gained weight during this part of the journey. I have no idea. I didn't weigh myself at all during that time. I do know that eventually, months later, all my clothes were getting too big, and today I am 75 pounds lighter than I was at my heaviest.

I knew it wasn't about the scale for me this time. My previous weight-loss efforts had been *all* about the scale. If I felt I was doing everything right and the scale didn't show a loss, then the scale was right and I had to do better. It told me whether it had been a good day or a bad day, and it also told me how to feel. If it was a loss, I was ecstatic. if it was a gain, I was ashamed, depressed, fat, ugly, worthless.

What made the difference? It was when I began to feed my wants and needs with things that would satisfy them. When I wanted intimacy, a long hug would do it; an apple fritter would not. When I wanted stress relief, a long walk with a friend would do it; twelve spoonfuls of frosting would not.

Once I learned to accept my needs and give myself what I really wanted and needed, I discovered the same principle applied to food. To satisfy true body hunger and let myself believe there was enough food in the world, I allowed myself to eat whatever I wanted, when I was hungry.

After a few weeks of eating "indulgent" foods, I asked myself what I really wanted to eat. I was surprised at the answer: green salad, fresh fruit, lean protein, and good bread. So that's what I ate. And amazing things happened.

I stopped wanting cookies and ice cream all the time. Do I still eat cookies and ice cream? Definitely … when that's what I really want. There are times when I think I want to eat the whole house, or at least a whole package of cookies, and I do my best to turn my awareness inside and figure out what I really want.

When I want to binge or eat more than I need, I now know it is not food that I really want. I will be feeding something that will never be satisfied with food. I need to *feel* my feelings, not *feed* my feelings. This awareness doesn't stop me every time, but after fifteen years of maintaining a healthy weight, consuming unhealthy amounts of food is the exception rather than the rule.

It's not that you need to give yourself every single thing you want—it's that you need to give yourself the choice every single time. As long as you are aware that it's your choice, you feel empowered and in control.

YOUR STORY STARTS NOW

I hate scales because of the power people give them. Your weight is only a number, just like your age. YOU ARE MORE THAN A NUMBER. You are an amazing human being.

Everyone has a story about how they became overweight. They're all different. It doesn't matter how you got where you are. What matters is where you choose to go from here.

The real issue of why you are overweight is not about the food. It is not about scales. It is not about your age. The real issue is you ... and your life choices.

> *"This time, like all times, is a very good one,*
> *if we but know what to do with it."*
> —Ralph Waldo Emerson

THE LITTLE HUNGER

Accept you have done the best you could with what you had.

Every day what you know changes, which means what you do can change. When you know better, you can do better. Accept that there is no magic! We all dream of the magic pill or silver bullet that will allow us to be thin, beautiful and happy forever. It doesn't exist. The only way to get there is to accept where you are now and then be free to move forward. There is no need to live the past over and over.

Accept that you can trust yourself and your body. Flip the true hunger switch back on. What does true body hunger feel like? This is when your body needs you to eat. This is the *little* hunger. What does it feel like for you? Remember, my answers will not be the same as yours, but I can tell you how it feels for me. I feel physically empty, a little lethargic, maybe light-headed, and my stomach growls. I go from being a little hungry to VERY hungry quickly. I need to accept that I cannot let it go too long or I start to feel like there is not enough food in the world to satisfy me.

Once we get our appropriate body hunger switch working then we need to accept that our body does know when to stop. On the other side of hunger we have satisfaction. There is one hitch here: It takes time for the message to get from your stomach to your brain that you are satisfied. Our mind needs time to catch up to our body. Accept that you are worth the time and energy to figure this all out.

People I work with say and write things like this: "I am tired of battling with my body." "My body is something I try not to pay attention to. It's too depressing when I really think about it." "I am sick of being consumed and obsessed with food and my body." So, we're either trying to ignore something or we're obsessed with it. People who struggle with food are notorious for their "all-or-nothing" approach not only to food, but also to the deepest part of themselves. Acceptance is walking down the middle of the road knowing we will visit both ends of the spectrum sometimes, but the visits will be the exceptions rather than the rule.

We all want positive change in our lives. Acceptance of where you are is necessary to be able to move forward and make true change happen in your life. Acceptance is about loving yourself and appreciating yourself wherever you are. Acceptance does not mean you want to stay where you are or that you even like it; it simply means you acknowledge where you are.

EAT WHAT YOU WANT

You deserve to feel proud of your choices every day. My biggest shame in life came from my relationship with food. I didn't want to be that person anymore.

When I tell people to eat what they want when they're hungry, the first thing they say is, "Are you serious? Anything I want? *Anything!?*"

You would think I had just thrown open the vault at Fort Knox and said, "Okay, take as many gold bars as you want." When I tell people to eat what they want, I routinely get bewildered looks and skeptical responses. We are so deprived and confused we can't make heads or tails of this statement. Most people walk into my Five Foundations class and sit down with a sigh, resigned to try another diet. "Maybe," they think to themselves, "this one *really* will work. I'll do anything she tells me."

Then I tell them to eat what they want when they're hungry, and the gloves come off.

"Are you *kidding*? I'll gain a million pounds! I have never allowed myself to eat anything I want! This is mind-boggling."

Outwardly, it would *appear* that these people—most of them overweight—do in fact allow themselves to eat anything their heart desires. They even believe it themselves, at least in the beginning.

But they don't. Elena recounted a lunch appointment when her client had a banana split for dessert. The banana split looked so good, but Elena wouldn't allow herself to have one. She fantasized about the banana split, but it would be "bad" to have it, so she resisted. Nine months after that lunch, Elena bought half a cake from the same restaurant but still would not allow herself to have a banana split. She was going to get just one piece of cake but learned it was only two dollars more to buy half a cake, so it seemed senseless to get only one piece. She ate the half a cake but still would not allow herself the banana split.

Why is it so astounding to be told we can eat what we want? One reason is because we are convinced we already give ourselves *too* much, and that is why we weigh so much. The problem is that we don't give ourselves what we really want, so we are not satisfied, and we continue to try to become satisfied. The bottom line is, we don't trust ourselves. We think we can't be trusted with food; if we could be trusted, we wouldn't be overweight. We think what we really want is "bad," so we create "forbidden foods." The truth is, there is no bad food. In labeling it "bad," the food only becomes more attractive. We need to eat what we want, when we're hungry.

Hunger is when you need to eat, so you need to become familiar with this sensation. The goal is to eat before becoming *too* hungry, because when we've gone too long without food, our choices become skewed. On the other hand, if we start to eat without experiencing actual body hunger, then nothing can satisfy, and we have no idea when to stop. This brings us back to moderation—not waiting to eat until we are ravenous or eating when we're not hungry.

Hunger. It feels a little different for everyone. It is about self-awareness. You want to start eating when you are feeling just the right amount of hunger. For some, at the first twinge of hunger is the best time to eat. For others, they can wait for more intense hunger and then eat. The trick is to eat when you feel you are setting yourself up for success instead of waiting too long and setting yourself up for disaster.

When you are truly hungry, you can eat what you really want. Nothing is off limits or "bad." We need to give ourselves what we really want or we will not be satisfied. And when we're not satisfied, we want more ...

In our minds, we tell ourselves certain foods are bad so we won't eat them. However, when we finally give in to eating those foods, we are surprised to find they're not even that good. For example, Elena went back to the restaurant—at my urging—and ordered the banana split she had been craving. She was shocked to realize she didn't like the way it tasted. In fact, she didn't even finish it! So often, the attractiveness of these foods is simply the result of our classifying them as forbidden.

The irony is that as adults, we have *always* been able to eat whatever we want, when we want it. I am simply giving you permission to listen to your body's wants, needs and desires and fulfill them. The thing is, you don't need permission from me, you just need permission from yourself.

"At the center of your being you have the answer;
you know who you are and you know what you want."
—Lao Tzu

WAKE UP

My friend Cassandra said, "When I slowed my life down I didn't go to sleep, I woke up." How do you stop eating when you are satisfied? You slow down. This is not a race. Take your time. Be *in* the moment of eating, savor every bite of food, put your utensils down, chew.

If you saw the movie *What About Bob?* you probably remember the dinner scene where Bob savors every bite of his food with quite a bit of enthusiasm. "Mmm, Mmmm, MmmmmmMm!" Bob shows gratitude for what he's been given and enjoys every morsel. You don't have to go into rapture with every bite, but you'll notice when you eat when you're hungry and what you really want, it is amazing how good it tastes.

One definition of satisfaction, in terms of eating, is the "absence of hunger." You are satisfied when you are no longer getting the hunger message from your body, even though you may still be getting it from your mouth, hands and brain.

Have you ever been in the middle of eating and been interrupted by a phone call or someone at the door? When you get back to your food, you realize you don't really want to finish it. In this case, you have let your mouth, hands and brain catch up with your body, and you know you're satisfied. The trick is to learn how to do this without being interrupted.

If you're eating something that doesn't taste good, stop. It's not what you really want. When most of us eat something we don't like, the next thought is, "What's next? That certainly didn't do it." Do what? It didn't satisfy you.

To be "in the moment" of eating, you need to focus, be awake, and eat slowly.

> *"Slow and steady wins the race."*
> —Aesop

HARA HACHI BU

Many times, when you can't figure out what to eat, it's because the hunger you are experiencing is not body hunger. You open every cupboard in the kitchen, peer into the refrigerator, looking for what will satisfy you. If you are hungering for affection or companionship or a release from stress or anything other than body hunger, you can eat and eat and eat and *never* be satisfied.

I use the "apple test" to determine if I'm body hungry or not. If an apple seems appealing, then I am really hungry. If I think, "No, not an apple, maybe a ..." then I know what I am experiencing is not body hunger. I am hungry for something else. Maybe a nap, a good cry, some company, a belly laugh ...

Okinawa has the healthiest and longest-living population in the world, and for the past forty years scientists have been trying to find out why. One of the findings is a concept called "hara hachi bu," which means "eight-tenths full." In Okinawa, eating and drinking until you are only 80 percent full is socially and culturally reinforced. In other words: everything in moderation. In other words: the opposite of what most of us do. In other words: life doesn't have to be "all or nothing." We can learn to walk down the middle of the road.

So many people live with an all-or-nothing approach not only with food but also with the deepest part of themselves. Hara hachi bu—which I define as living, eating and being in moderation—is walking down the middle of the road knowing we will visit both ends of the spectrum sometimes, but that will be the exception rather than the rule. Living on the pendulum of extremes is a hard existence.

When I was pregnant for the first time and working with a wonderful midwife, I asked her about diet soda. It was a daily treat for me, and I really enjoyed it. I dejectedly mentioned that I knew she was going to tell me to go "cold turkey" and stop drinking diet soda. I was in for a pleasant surprise. She smiled at me and said, "Linda, everything in moderation. One diet soda a day is not going to harm the baby. Just think, *everything* in moderation."

Moderation in all things is a concept I had been learning as I lived my two promises but had not put into words. Of course I had heard it a million times, but for some reason, this time I heard it and internalized it as a personal mantra and way of life.

A typical person struggling with food and weight will ping pong back and forth between what I call "survivor hungry" (after the TV show)—when a rat runs in front of you and you consider eating it, and "Thanksgiving full"— no explanation needed.

We are "starving" when we start to eat and feel like there's not enough food in the world to satisfy us. Fast and furious and almost unconsciously, we gulp the food down until we realize we are stuffed. We stop eating but continue to get even more full as what we consumed settles in to our stomachs.

Now we are so full that we swear we are never going to eat again. Well, maybe we'll skip a meal. Then guess what? We're back to ... starving!

Hara hachi bu is about balance. It is about eating in moderation, drinking in moderation, working in moderation, playing in moderation, sleeping in moderation ... living in moderation.

One aspect of your life does not take over your whole life. When you start a new relationship, you don't neglect every other relationship in your life. You balance it with your other relationships.

Hara hachi bu is the answer to so many things. Moderation is not very sexy. It is not a quick fix. But it works. Before I figured this out, I was exhausted from the extreme highs and extreme lows in my life. I was ready to live in a sane way. Hara hachi bu is the most sane way I can think of living.

It is possible to live, eat and be in moderation. Hara hachi bu.

> *"To know when you have enough*
> *is to be rich beyond measure."*
> —Lao Tzu

YOU CONTROL YOU

So many people say to me, "Linda, I am out of control with food. I am just out of control." Most people say they want "control" over their eating. The reality is, unless you are on a feeding tube, you *are* the one feeding yourself. You are the one putting the food into your mouth. No one is forcing you to do it. The moment you accept you are in control, you have begun to take responsibility. And you will realize that saying, "I'm out of control," is not a true statement and does not give you license to overeat.

You are in control—only you get to choose what you put in your mouth and your mind and your heart. So when you want to use being "out of control" as an excuse to drown yourself in food, instead, make a new choice and begin to deal with the real issue: feeding the big hunger.

Think about a child's reaction when as adult says, "Don't touch that." Most of the children I know, including myself when I was a child, would immediately touch the forbidden object. There's a deep part of us that needs to know it's our choice. We are in control. We are in control of what we touch ... and what we eat.

LISTEN TO YOURSELF

When I teach the Five Foundations I hear over and over, "I was fine until I started dieting. Then I started doubting my choices and criticizing myself for not being good enough. And then wham—all I was thinking about was food and what I would eat next and what would be the best choice and how "good" I was going to be." When we stop doing what comes naturally and enforce an artificial action that doesn't feel good and is difficult to sustain, we are bound to eventually go "off" the regimen, only to think we need another regimen, a better one, one that will work better. We need to stop and think. We need to get off the vicious cycle of being "good" or "on" and then being "bad" or "off." We need to just "be."

For people who are struggling to lose weight, there seems to be a disconnect between the mind and body. All communication between the two is stopped. We figure this situation is just the way it's going to be, so we'll take ourselves out of the picture and do what someone else says will work. The Five Foundations are different. They don't tell you what to do; they help you tell yourself what to do. The Five Foundations work from the inside out. They are about reconnecting the mind and body. They are about self-awareness, self-trust and self-respect.

Dieters have listened to so many people for so long that we assume we must not have the answer for ourselves. We have read so many magazines and books and newspaper articles that tell us the "right" way to lose weight and get healthy, we are convinced that we do not have the answer for ourselves. We have looked in the mirror with disgust, bought bigger clothes and felt out of control so many times that we somehow believe there is no way we might have the answer for ourselves.

Are you ready? You have the answer. Your body has the answer. Your heart has the answer. Your soul has the answer. You need to listen to receive the answer. Common sense tells us that if we ate only when we were hungry and stopped eating when we were no longer hungry, we would lose weight. And this is true. We don't need to make things complicated. I am a simple person, and I need simple instructions. None of the: "Simple 27-Step-Process" for me. Five I can handle—so the Five Foundations were born out of my need to understand the simplicity of listening to and trusting my body.

BUILD NEW HABITS

No matter who we are or where we grew up, there are many kinds of admonitions we hear day after day:

"That's not the right way."

"Oh, you don't want to do that."

"I know you'll be happier if you ..."

When we hear these words often enough and for long enough, what is the result? It's simple! We start to believe that maybe we don't know the right answers for ourselves. We stop trusting our own answers and look to others instead of ourselves.

That's why there are always so many self-improvement books on the best-seller list; we believe they have the answers, not us. We are so sure somewhere out there, someone else has the answers for us.

I am totally in favor of reading everything you can get your hands on. But as you read, you need to also be listening inside of yourself.

Take it all in and then decide whether it applies to you or not. Listen to your gut. Become aware of the intuition we all have, and listen to it. Get back in touch with who you really are and what you really want. Then trust that you know what's best for you.

You can trust yourself. You can trust your body. Listen. Be aware.

British ships have something called the "still" signal. When this signal goes off, everyone on the ship must stop, pause, assess the situation, and then prepare to do the wise thing. We need to develop our own "still" signal so we can learn to stop, pause, assess, and prepare to do the wise thing. Otherwise, we get into a reactive mode where we are not assessing and preparing to take action—we are just reacting. Part of building your trust within yourself and breaking away from old habits is to give yourself the time and space to choose your plan of action.

One of the best ways to become more aware is to question yourself. The questions are not for your friend or neighbor or significant other, but for you to ask yourself.

"How do I want to treat this situation?"

"What do I want to think about it?"

"What do I want to do?"

Habits are habits because they happen automatically. Before you even realize you've made a choice, you're halfway through it. Positive change happens when you stop yourself and take the time to figure out what you'd like to have happen. Habits become habits because we do them over and over and over. To develop new habits, we need to become aware of what we want and then practice it over and over and over.

> *"Practice is the best of all instructors."*
> —Publilius Syrus Maxim

BE COMPASSIONATE

You *will* eat things that make you feel crappy, you *will* make choices you don't feel good about, and you *will* do things that move you further away from your goals. Still, be compassionate with yourself. Beating yourself up does NO good. I used to beat myself up black and blue—daily—and to no avail. I was still binging, I was still sneaking food, I was still fat, and I was still unhappy. Sitting yourself down for a stern talking-to will not help you improve. Giving yourself the benefit of the doubt and talking to yourself positively will.

Some people think being compassionate with yourself is looking at life through rose-colored glasses. I think of it more as looking at life the way I want to. There are always multiple ways to see everything. I choose to see myself and others in the best light possible. Everyone else is doing the best they can as well. If people are rude to me, I know they must be having a hard day or maybe even a hard life. There is no sense in my being rude in response. Being rude doesn't make anyone feel any better.

WHERE ATTENTION GOES, ENERGY FLOWS

The things we can't explain are usually the most powerful and profound. I couldn't explain to people why I lost so much weight. I couldn't explain why food became a nonissue for me (most of the time). I couldn't explain why my marriage and children were so wonderful. These things just happened.

Though I may not be able to explain these things, I now believe I know why they happened: the law of attraction. When my mind was full of food and what I shouldn't eat and how I hated my overweight body, my thoughts attracted those things, and that became my reality. When my mind was full of thoughts that I would never find a wonderful man to spend my life with—no one appeared.

My thoughts, my feelings about the future, and my actions all led me to a terrible place—in my life and in myself.

Slowly I began to practice thinking and feeling and acting differently. Now my mind is full of respect and gratitude for my healthy, strong body. My mind is full of loving thoughts about my husband and the two children we were blessed with. My mind is full of the possibilities of creating my own business. My mind is full of gratitude for our sweet home and wonderful family and friends. And things just keep getting better.

I believe and think and act on the fact that life is getting better every day. And you know what? My life truly does get better every day.

We attract what we dwell on—where we put our energy and attention. We attract those things into our lives.

Even though I can't fully explain what the law of attraction is and how it works, I would never go back to my old way of thinking. Why? Because I was pretty miserable before I formed a habit of positive thinking. Whether the fulfillment I experience now is because I attracted it or created it—or for some other reason—I have peace of mind and a positive outlook that life will continue to get better.

Will bad things happen in my life? Yes. How do I know? Because they happen in everyone's life. But I choose to put as little energy and attention into them as possible.

YOUR BEST IS ALL YOU CAN DO

Years ago I walked in the door and my daughter Olivia came running toward me and threw herself into my arms sobbing. She explained through sobs that she had had to move her behavior pin on the chart in her classroom from green to yellow because I forgot to sign her assignment book.

I immediately apologized for not signing and then gently reminded her that the reason I had not signed it was because she had not given the assignment book to me. I told her it would be the only time, and that she wouldn't have to move her pin again for the rest of the year! In my eyes, this would be a great accomplishment. Olivia then explained that during the previous year she had never had to move from green to yellow, and now she would not have a perfect year.

Perfection—wow, that's hard to beat! I explained that third grade was going to be different than second grade, probably harder, and we didn't want to shoot for perfection. We wanted to do the best we could.

A lesson for all of us: You can only expect yourself to do the very best you can with what you have. The teacher did not know that the day before had been Olivia's big brother's tenth birthday, and we had a house full of children and adults and games and food and so many different things that led us to forgetting the assignment book. It was only the fifth day of school, and we were still working into the routine. We had done the best we could.

Perfection ... all or nothing. A place I lived for many, many years. The United States seems to reinforce this idea. People take pride in being workaholics: "I work too much and am proud of it." The most coveted cars are either Humvee size or Mini size. Extremes are the American way of life—the opposite of hara hachi bu—and not how I choose to live my life.

THERE IS NO "WRONG"

The Five Foundations are scariest for people who don't trust themselves. I was that person once. Some days I am still that person.

When I feel like I am doing things "wrong" and am losing faith in myself, I do some reflecting, talking and writing about what's going on.

Usually I have had an indulgent week or two and am not liking the way my clothes are fitting and the way I am feeling: lethargic, heavy, a little depressed.

The last indulgent period started with my birthday, which I *love*. On other holidays, there are other people celebrating, but birthdays are all about celebrating the day *you* entered the world. (When people complain about another birthday—another year older—I tell them there is only one other option: I'll take the birthday!)

Cake with frosting is one of my favorite indulgences—love it, LOVE it, **LOVE IT!** On my last birthday, we had a barbecue. There was delicious steak, salad, and lots of other things I didn't really want, like a macaroni salad, baked potatoes, and rolls.

My aunt said to me, "Aren't you going to try my macaroni salad? I thought you, out of everyone, would try it. It's healthy." In the past, I would have felt compelled to try some because my aunt had made the macaroni salad expecting me to eat it. I mumbled something and went back to eating my delicious steak and salad. Then the cake—now *this* was worth it!!!! I enjoyed three pieces of my birthday cake and savored every bite. It only comes once a year, and I wanted to enjoy it. My aunt still speaks to me even though I didn't have the macaroni salad. Everyone ended up happy. Especially me.

The three pieces of birthday cake marked a starting point. During the next two weeks, I ate my favorite donut (filled with frosting, what a surprise) for my birthday, went out for a birthday breakfast, had a birthday lunch, and indulged in a couple of birthday dinners. I didn't feel so great.

I pulled my favorite jeans out of the dryer (they *do* shrink in there), and they were tighter than I felt comfortable wearing. I did some deep knee bends, a couple of lunges and—the jeans were still too tight. The doubts began to crash in. How can I be writing a book about being healthy and losing weight when I can't even fit in my favorite jeans?!?! Am I headed right back to 215 pounds? Is it all over?

I found myself in that world of all or nothing: I'm either perfect or I'm a mess. I'm on a "diet," doing the "plan," following the "program"—or "I'm a pig." The opposite of hara hachi bu.

To get back to a more moderate mentality, I spent a weekend talking to my husband, my friends, and myself. It became clear—even as I wrote this chapter—that I was going to be just fine. Indulgence can be a good thing ... but for now, for me, it's over.

We always get to choose. I chose to get up at 6:00 a.m., go for a run, come home, spend time with my children, get them ready for school, have oatmeal for breakfast with my husband and then sit down, with my green tea, to write. I put on my *second*-favorite pair of jeans and felt good. I will be in my favorite jeans at some point. It's going to be okay. I can trust myself to make the choices that will bring me health and a life I love.

FOOD IS FUEL

In a previous section, I shared how I lived on chocolate chip cookies and pancakes for quite a while. Now I am telling you that food is fuel. Food is not love, food is not companionship, food is not celebration. Food is fuel. When my husband Kelly told me food just "fills the hole" and that the only reason he ate was to fill up his stomach, I just about keeled over. I thought, are you kidding me?! Food is everything. And up till that point in my life, it really had been. Everything was about food.

When Kelly told me food is fuel, I realized that I had been confusing the big hunger and the little hunger. Things I put into my stomach would not feed the big hunger. Food doesn't bring love, it doesn't bring joy, it doesn't bring a feeling of fulfillment. It just fills the physical hole called your stomach. It provides the nutrition your body needs, *and that is all it does*. Food is fuel. We can choose to fill that hole with food that is creative, fun and enjoyable, but remember, it's still just filling the hole.

I don't live on chocolate chip cookie dough and pancakes anymore because I don't want to. For one thing, I *feel* better when I eat wholesome foods as a rule and "indulgence foods" as the exception. For another thing, I have a lot to live for right now, and my health is very important to me. I could tell you I have oatmeal and berries every morning for breakfast and I love it, but if you don't like oatmeal with berries, that means it's not the breakfast for you. I could tell you that fruits and vegetables are soooo great for you in so many different ways. But until you find fruits and vegetables you like and *want* to eat, they will not be a part of your regular eating.

Food is fuel. When you put crappy fuel in, you usually end up feeling crappy. When you put good fuel in, you usually end up feeling good. It's your choice. There is no wrong or bad—only what works for you. I have had people argue with me about the Five Foundations. "I *like* to eat fast, I don't want to eat slowly." My response is, that's fine. Eat fast. There is no wrong. As long as you feel good about what you're doing, and it's moving you closer to your goals, go for it.

Your body will naturally begin to crave things that will bring you better health. Pay attention to how the food makes you feel—physically and emotionally. By paying attention, you will gain knowledge about the foods that work for you. If a particular food makes you feel energetic and happy to tell someone you consumed it, you can choose to eat it again. If a food you eat brings guilt and a physically sick feeling, remember to eat less of it next time or choose not to eat it again at all. It's been said that knowledge is power. I believe knowledge is potential: Until action is taken on the knowledge, it is only potential. With action comes the true power.

You have the power to learn, listen and discover what works for your body, mind and soul. Don't give away that power to anyone ... no matter what magic they claim to have. You have the magic for *you*.

IS THIS THING STILL FLYING?

I will never forget reading about the Apollo 12 space capsule. When it was struck by lightning, astronaut Alan Bean had to act fast. He remembered the question test pilots are trained to ask when something goes wrong: "Is this thing still flying?" This question helps the pilot stop panicking and start assessing the situation. For the Apollo 12, the spacecraft was still headed for the moon. So, one by one, Alan Bean dealt with the warning lights until everything was fine.

We need to ask ourselves the same question: "Is this thing still flying?" Are you doing the best you can? That's all you can expect of yourself. In the face of loss or setbacks, we can decide *not* to add frustration, disappointment, and hopelessness to the situation. Give yourself the benefit of the doubt. Trust that you will "right" yourself. You can change your course at any time—if you choose.

IT'S UP TO YOU

You can let your life run you, or you can run your life. Letting your life run you means allowing yourself to be drawn to what appears to be the most urgent or important thing without giving it any thought. This is a small-picture way of living. We need to back up and take a look at the big picture every once in a while. What's important to *you*? If everything is important, then nothing is important.

Humans have the privilege of not just surviving in the world; we also have the option to *thrive*. Your choices day in and day out move you closer to one or the other. Are you thriving or surviving? I once worked with someone who answered the question "How are you?" with the same answer every time: "Surviving." To me, surviving is the lowest level of living. It's one step above being dead.

Thriving is up to you. You cannot delegate your life experiences or feelings to anyone else. My daughter had a preschool teacher who would always ask me to exercise for her when I was on my way to work out. She would say, "Hey, run for me too." "Sure," I would say and laugh. Then I would go do the only thing that was possible, work out in *my* body, for *my* health and *my* own sense of well-being.

You may think it sounds silly to ask someone else to do your exercise for you, but think about this: How many times do we try to give someone else the responsibility for our feelings about ourselves, or our decisions about food?

"You made me feel..."

"I didn't want to have the macaroni salad, but she insisted..."

No one can make you feel anything about yourself or choose anything without your cooperation. I can take care of what I feel, and I can choose what I eat, but no one can do that for me. And they can't do it for you, either! Part of awareness is realizing that you alone make the choices that face you every single day. Nobody chooses for you.

Many of us try to skip the work of figuring out what we want and need. We just want to hit the fast-forward button to feeling good. There are many ways of feeling good in the moment: food, alcohol, drugs ... and many people abuse them.

Perhaps you are one of those people. That doesn't make you a bad person. If you recognize that you are hitting the fast-forward button, then you are already on the journey to awareness.

It takes courage to look inside yourself and figure out what you *really* want. When we look inside, we see things that scare us—that are so different from anything we are used to—and we panic. It takes courage and hard work to grow as a person. When you are living your life on purpose, that is what you are doing—growing.

This may be news to you. You have been growing all along, and you have grown to where you are right now. Life did not just happen to you. The choices you have made each day have put you where you are.

"Know your truth, speak your truth,
live your truth."
—Eileen Hannegan

YOU ARE A LIGHT

Gerald Jampolsky does an exercise where he calls up someone from the audience and then stands in front of the person and looks at them. According to Jampolsky, this is how most of us look at each other: we look at bodies and faces and think we are truly looking at the person.

Then Jampolsky takes a candle and holds it in front of the volunteer's face. He looks at the person through the candle. Soon all he sees is the light of the candle.

Jampolsky is asking us to start looking at people for what they are: light. When we look at people, we need to see the light they have inside of them.

We all have a light—we all *are* a light. We can feed the flame and have it grow strong and bright, or we can squelch it and keep it as small as possible. I believe we can never put out our light completely. There is always a spark in there somewhere.

> *"While there's life, there's hope."*
> —Cicero

WHAT DO YOU WANT?

No matter how long it has been since you were in touch with what makes you laugh and smile and feel contentment, you can get there. We need to stop waking up every day and saying to ourselves, "I can't wait for this day to be over," or, "I can't wait for the weekend," or, "I can't wait for my vacation." Let's start enjoying life—every day of it. Let's start making our dreams come true.

To be in a place where we can make our dreams come true, we need to take care of ourselves. We need to be in the right frame of mind: positive, confident, and full of faith in ourselves.

Get in touch with yourself. Know your wants, needs, and desires. Develop awareness of your emotions, awareness of your hunger, awareness of what you want, awareness of your body, and awareness of your environment.

To make progress, we need to pay attention.

Where your mind goes, your body follows. If you have clarity in your thoughts, you will be focused in your actions. The only thing standing between you and your wants, needs, and desires is being mindful and being purposeful.

The crazy thing is that your mind doesn't pick up the "negative" part of your statements. If you think, "I will not have a brownie," guess what your brain gets stuck on? A brownie! Tell yourself what you do want, not what you don't want. Where your mind goes, your body follows.

YOUR BEST-CASE SCENARIO

A psychologist recently told me about one of the methods she uses in working with people. She has her patients draw a picture of their worst-case scenario for life and then explain the picture to her. The patients get right to work and draw all kinds of details about their worst fears and all the disasters the future might hold. After they explain their drawing, she has them draw a picture of their best-case scenario for life. She then asks them to explain the drawing to her. This assignment is more difficult than the first one. People struggle to draw positive things and to express a vision of what their best life might look like.

For some reason, it seems easier and more acceptable to be negative. In society, it is common to speak negatively, think negatively, act negatively—even to draw negatively. The focus on what we don't want is reinforced socially. A group of friends get together and they all start to complain. Then it becomes almost a competition: who has the worst, hardest life of all?

A long time ago, I decided not to spend time with people who complain. Life is too short to be pulled down by the negative energy of those around you. One of the best things you can do is to surround yourself with people who bring out the best in you and make you feel great about future possibilities in life.

YOU ALWAYS HAVE A CHOICE

Each of us has choices to make. Every day, day in and day out, we make choices. You always have a choice. You can choose to put this book down and not read it. You can choose to believe that the principles in this book can make a difference in your life. You can choose to disagree with me: "Oh, she doesn't know my life, I *do not* have a choice." You can choose and choose and choose—and still tell yourself you have no choice.

Well, today *is* a new day full of choices. Today *can* be different, if you choose. The hardest part is accepting that you alone are responsible for taking care of yourself. Many people wait for someone to rescue them or tell them the secret of life. The truth is, you are the only one that can know for yourself. There is only one way to know, and that is to try and try again.

> *"The strongest principle of growth*
> *lies in human choice."*
> —George Eliot

ANYTHING IS POSSIBLE

I have formed a new identity: dog lover. For the first forty years of my life, I always had cats but never liked dogs. We recently got two puppies, and I am in shock at how I became a dog lover overnight.

In the past, I thought dogs were just big, noisy, stinky hairballs. Now, every dog is cute and lovable. Talk about an identity change!

I never thought I would have one dog, much less two and be in love with every dog I see. Anything is possible.

HOW I JOINED THE DOG OWNER'S CLUB

Every time you say, "I am ..." you are creating and reinforcing your identity. It seemed unbelievable, but I am now a dog lover. I never imagined having a dog. I find it incredible that I am watching my two puppies romp around in the backyard after they just took a nap.

Many serendipitous events led my husband and me to reconsider our no-dog stance. For example, calamity struck and Kelly's mother passed away in New Zealand. He went home to New Zealand to be with his four siblings and dad for two weeks and help with the service. Our children Keegan and Olivia and I needed to stay in Hawaii because the school year had just begun and I had a lot of teaching and speaking engagements.

During that time, Olivia and I starting talking about how a puppy might help the healing process. We thought it would be sweet to get a little girl puppy and name her Iris, after Kelly's mum. We could have Iris waiting and she could kiss all Kelly's tears away when he got home.

I told one of my dear friends about our plan. She thought that surprising Kelly with a puppy may not make for the best homecoming, so she brought over a "practice puppy" for us. It was a stuffed dog. We didn't get too much practice with it, but it was the sweetest gesture.

When Kelly came home, we told him about the puppy that almost was. He laughed and said, "Thank goodness you didn't do that." The next day, he took the day off, and while the kids were at school the two of us went to have lunch at Kelly's favorite sushi restaurant—which happens to be right by a pet store.

After we finished lunch, we wandered that direction and saw a group of three adorable puppies wrestling together. Though they were from the same litter, they all looked different. One was black with a docked tail and looked pure Chihuahua. One looked like a cocker spaniel and was dark brown and white with sweet freckles on his nose and a crooked tail (botched docking job). One was light brown with a white chest, a long black tail, and the sweetest beagle face you have ever seen.

The puppies were supposedly Chihuahua-Pug, but there was no guarantee on the breed … go figure.

We thought the one that looked like a beagle was too sweet. He was wagging his tail so hard at us that he almost fell over. I looked at Kelly and said, "Let's just hold him." Though I fully expected him to say no, he said, "Okay." I found an employee to let us into the puppy meeting room. Kelly and I held the puppy, loved him, and decided the kids should get a chance to meet him before we made a decision. We asked the pet store to put him on hold for us, but they explained it was not possible. We left with the understanding that if the puppy was there when we got back, then it was meant to be.

The way it worked out, we took three more trips to the pet store.

Finally, we worked up the nerve to buy the puppy and enter the "Dog Owners Club." As we left, I just kept shaking my head and saying, "I can't believe we have a dog, I can't believe we have a dog."

We brought the puppy home and named him Copper. Before long, I began to reason that if one dog is great (which it most certainly is), then two would be better, right? Plus, I was feeling terrible leaving Copper alone at home. So, two months after we got Copper, we started looking for another dog. Olivia wanted a smaller dog of her own, so we got Satchel, an eight-week-old Terrier–Chihuahua. He weighs two pounds and has legs up to his neck. We almost named him Prancer because his long legs and the way he walks make him look like a prancing reindeer.

Seeing our two dogs play together is pure joy. Satchel is like a miniature of Copper. He can stand up right underneath Copper's belly. They were fast friends, after just three days of knowing each other. And I can leave the house feeling a little less guilt than before.

The way our lives take shape can be such a shock. How many times have I thought, "If you would've told me five years ago, or two months ago, or yesterday that I'd be ... I would've told you to shut uuup!"

Our family's experience in becoming dog owners speaks to the possibility in all of us. I've learned that saying, "I will never do this ..." or "I will never be that ..." can make you wrong. At one point, I had said I would never live in Hawaii, and now I can't imagine living anywhere else. I had said I would never be a dog owner, and now I have two. What else have I closed myself off to that I may benefit from some day?

Stay open.

> *"When I let go of who I am,*
> *I became what I might be."*
> —Lao Tzu

WHO ARE YOU?

Your identity is more than the roles you play in life; it is who you are. It is the core of you. I am a person who has lost weight and will keep it off forever. That is now part of my identity.

It is strange when people meet me and say, "Wow, I could never imagine you being overweight." That is mind-boggling to me because it is such a part of who I am. I am a person who once weighed 215 pounds. I am a person who perseveres through adversity. I am happy. I love quotes. I am open to learning and discovering every day. I am loud. I am a person who eats only when I'm hungry. I laugh freely. I am a person learning hara hachi bu.

Of course, this is just the beginning of who I am.

I love to read. I am a voracious reader. It is almost impossible to imagine myself as someone who never reads. If I didn't like the fact that I read all the time, then I could begin to change that identity. I could empty my environment of reading material. I could refrain from picking up a book or newspaper. I could start to believe I can be a non-reader and then say to myself every day, "I am a person who doesn't read." I am not going to do this, but it is possible. It is possible to change our identity.

Besides becoming a dog lover, I have changed my identity in another way recently. In the past, I was someone who loved a cold beer or a good glass of red wine. I also was a person who didn't usually stop at one. As a result, I have had many hangovers and headaches, and I have done some things I am not proud of.

At my son's thirteenth birthday party I had spent the day cleaning and preparing for the party and not eating very much. It was a hot August night in Hawaii. I consumed four light beers and loved every sip, but didn't eat much dinner. As a result, when everyone left I felt terrible. So terrible that I spent most of the night in the bathroom with my head in the toilet. Not a pretty picture I know, but I am making a point here. This was not the first time this had happened.

As I lay on the cool tile floor of the bathroom waiting not to feel miserable, I started to think back on the number of times I had had more to drink than I needed. I realized I had been drinking for twenty years and couldn't think of a single way it had improved who I am. The first twenty years of my life I didn't drink, the next twenty years of my life I did … it was time to stop.

Many times before I had thought about stopping, but drinking was relaxing and tasted good and was fun to do with friends. Until that night in the bathroom, I had never been so clear and decisive about it. This time I really decided to stop.

The next morning I announced to Kelly that I was not going to drink for the next year. He smiled a knowing smile that said, "Yeah, right." So I told him the whole decision-making episode and tried to convince him of my resolve. Do you know how you convince someone (including yourself) that you're going to change? You do it simply by changing your behavior.

That first day after the decision, I probably told myself a hundred times: "I don't drink. Did I tell you I'm not drinking for the next year? I am a person who doesn't drink. That's me, a non-drinker. Did you hear? I'm not drinking."

I was beginning to change my identity, and it took some effort. The first two weeks were especially difficult. Then there was the first social engagement ... and then the first family gathering ... and then the first holiday. With each day and each experience and each get-together, I changed my identity a little more.

So many people don't realize you can *change* your identity. A woman recently told me, "I'm going on vacation and will probably gain five pounds." I told her I always lost weight when I went on vacation. She decided that she would go on vacation and say to herself over and over, "I am a person who loses weight on vacation." She came back from her vacation two pounds lighter.

We get to be whomever we choose. There is no right or wrong. There is only what's real and right and true for you. This is not about judgment; it is about being the person you want to be.

> *"I exist as I am, that is enough."*
> —Walt Whitman

KNOWING LEADS TO DOING

I talk to people almost daily who say things like, "I just woke up one day and asked myself, 'How did I end up here?'" or, "I looked in the mirror this morning and didn't recognize the person looking back. How did this happen?" It's incredibly easy just to be swept away by life and to do what others think we should do. Then one day we wake up to a reality that takes us by surprise.

Always remember that you have been making choices, and that those choices have led to your present reality—even if you look back and realize they were not the choices you would make today. This simply means you are growing and becoming more aware!

There is nothing that feels better than taking care of yourself. And I don't mean doing it because someone—your doctor, your spouse, your mother, your best friend—told you to or said you should, but because you feel good about who you are and deserve to be taken care of.

Think about what it feels like when you are eating good-tasting, nourishing food you worked to prepare, when you are appropriately hungry and sharing a meal with someone you care about (which can sometimes mean eating all by yourself!)—there is no better feeling. And then you ask yourself, "Why don't I do this more often?"

Or this: instead of hitting snooze, roll out of bed and get out in the fresh air just as the sun is rising. As you move your body and wake up with nature, you marvel at the beauty and stillness. Again comes the question, "Why don't I do this more often?"

Perhaps most challenging of all: You carve time out of a regular busy day to be with yourself and concentrate on the "big picture" of your life and get clear about something that has been muddy. And surely then you think, "Why don't I do this more often?"

The answer to that question, and to this very common predicament, is true awareness.

To be truly aware means awareness of your wants and needs, awareness of what you're telling yourself, awareness of the people you are surrounding yourself with. Awareness leads to enlightenment and growth and a life that you love every day.

Each of us is a completely unique person. There is no one else exactly like you. That is why only you can know the answers for yourself. A lot of times we think we know, but *real knowing is followed by doing!*

If I had a dollar for every time someone said to me, "I know what I need to do," but then wasn't doing it, I would be very rich. In fact, when I ask people, "Do you know why you are not moving closer to what you want?" they often reply, "Well, I know what I need to do, but ..."

There's a Zen saying, "To know and not do is to not yet know." We may think we know, but if we are not taking action, then we don't know well enough—we don't yet know. You know yourself better than anyone else. You know, somewhere inside of you, what you need to do.

Even when we know what our gut tells us, and what every hair on the back of our neck tells us, still we don't *do* it. Why? There are a few reasons, but to me, most of them boil down to putting others before ourselves. I won't do what I know is right for me because I don't want to put someone else out, or make them feel bad, or do something to upset them. Or, I need to put my child, spouse, sibling, cousin, or boss before myself because they really need me. Or, I'm sure I will have time to do what I know I need to do later, but for right now I will do what (fill in the blank) is asking.

Somewhere inside of you, you know that when you take care of *you*, you do a better job taking care of anyone and everyone who needs you. I know, I know... you know. Self-trust is at the heart of the Five Foundations. Listen to yourself. Trust yourself. Know that having knowledge is a wonderful thing, but using that knowledge leads to true success. Let's make a decision to *do* all the things we know we need to do.

IT'S ONLY A PROBLEM IF YOU SEE IT
THAT WAY

Beth had just purchased her dream house. She was excited about every aspect of her new home ... except when she looked into the backyard. Every time she looked in the backyard, all she saw was the plumeria tree right in the middle of the yard.

You see, one of the main reasons she and her husband had purchased the home was for their two small children. But with the tree in the middle of the yard, there would be no throwing a ball from one end to the other, no games running from one end to the other. The tree blocked the way. The tree was a problem. There was no way around it ... the tree ruined the backyard.

One day as Beth was walking though the yard with a new gardener, she mentioned how sad she was that the plumeria tree was in the middle of the backyard. The gardener looked at her and said matter-of-factly, "We can move it if you'd like."

She couldn't believe it. The tree could be moved? She had never even considered the option of moving the tree.

She had assumed it was in the way, and that was just the way it was.

Well, not many days later, the tree was moved to a corner of the backyard. The children can now play and run without obstruction. Now Beth is wondering what other "plumeria trees" there are in her life. What are the other things that seem impossible to change?

THE ONLY TWO CHOICES

I had a workshop recently and told the participants that for each goal we have, there are really only two options: You can give up, or you can keep trying. Five minutes later, someone asked, "Are there really only two options?"

It is so simple—you stop or you go, you say yes or you say no, you give up or you keep trying. Even if you say maybe, until you make a yes-or-no decision, nothing will happen. And who wants to live in "maybe"?

Do you want to grow a life you love? Do you want to become a person you are proud of? Only you can make that happen. Decide and take action toward who you want to be and where you want to be. Don't let the fear of making a mistake paralyze you. A mistake has no power over you. The next choice is always yours.

There are always only two choices: give up or keep trying.

DECIDE AND DO

Abby announced she wasn't going to talk to anyone about losing weight anymore. She wasn't going to talk with her husband or her daughters or her friends because she had been talking about it for so long and not doing it that they were all bored with it. Then she paused and laughed and said, *"I* am bored with it! I am ready to shut up and do it."

We talk and talk and talk but we don't do, and then we explain and defend and justify *why* we haven't done it, but we're going to do it. We *are* going to do it. It's strange, because I know with every fiber of my being that I am going to publish this book, yet I keep allowing things to get in the way.

Not giving up on what we want is so key. Even if you've tried a hundred million times, it can be done. Those were all practice times. Those times that we didn't do it were necessary to get to the time that we actually do it. All those times were practice.

Very few people that I know actually set out to do something and get it on the first try exactly the way they wanted or expected it.

I had a teacher conference with my sixth grade daughter's teacher, and it was what going exactly as I had expected it to. Then her teacher looked at me and said, "There's one thing I would like you to teach Olivia." I was all ears. Flashcards, drills, practice—whatever it was, I would help Olivia learn it. Then her teacher continued, "I would like you to teach Olivia that it is okay to be wrong." I was stunned. This was not what I expected at all. Having always been a person who wants to be right and works to be right and really likes to be right, this was a big assignment. The best way to teach something is to role model it and to believe it. Those were two areas I myself needed to work on: Being okay—perhaps happy—with being wrong and *believing* that it was a good thing.

Chris Evert says she learned more from her failures than from her successes. She is not the only incredibly successful person I have heard say that. I so admire people who can not only accept that being wrong is a good thing but that it is better than being right. For many of us, that kind of approach is truly a stretch. I teach people to keep trying and never to give up. I guess in a sense that is what I am saying. All those practice times were not successful at being "right," but they got you closer to what will be right.

"One good wish changes nothing,
one good decision changes everything."
—unknown

JUST ASK

One day as I finished an early morning run, I noticed there was an elderly woman I'd never seen before at the end of our road shuffling along slowly. I said good morning to her, and she looked at me with concerned eyes and asked, "Where is Kalama Street?" I said, "It's right there" and pointed across the street. She looked and started to head off slowly and unsteadily in the direction I pointed. I immediately decided to accompany her across the street. As I took her elbow to steady her, I asked if she was out for a morning walk. She replied, "Yes, but just walking, not running like you." I smiled. I told her I thought it was great she was out walking.

As we got to the other side of the street she stopped and just looked around. For the first time I realized she might truly be lost, not just a little turned around. So I said, "Here, let's walk down your street. You live on Kalama?" After a few steps she said, "Yes, yes, I do." We walked a little more and I gently asked which house was hers. She looked at me, smiled and rattled off her address. I told her that I would love to walk her all the way to her door if she didn't mind. She told me she would be fine and thanked me for the help. I told her to have a wonderful day and headed home.

As I was walking home I thought about how often we lose our way in life, and all we have to do is ask a few simple questions to find our way back to a smiling, familiar, strong place. But often we don't. The friend I made yesterday did not hesitate to ask for help. I said good morning, and she asked for the help she needed. She got what she needed—help home. Why did she get that help? Because she asked for it.

How often could you use some help, assistance, guidance, coaching … but you don't ask?

We all sometimes feel the weight of the world on our shoulders because the weight of *our* world is on our shoulders. It is a very nice feeling to take that weight off once in a while and not be in charge of the world.

All you have to do is ask.

We were not meant to go through this world alone. Surround yourself with friends, loved ones, family members, neighbors, anyone that makes you smile, brings out the best in you, and makes the weight of the world feel a little lighter.

Life is too short to spend being lost. Ask for directions. Make a map. Get some help, and then find your own way. Believe me, it's worth it.

USE YOUR SIGNALS

If you open your mind, there are usually endless possibilities and choices you can make. But you must first open your mind. Many times, just by voicing the situation someone else can give us perspective we wouldn't have reached on our own.

Lisa was driving and trying to change lanes so she could exit the freeway. She drove slowly and patiently, waiting for an opening in traffic. She waited and waited. Finally, she said to her daughter, "I'm going to miss the exit because I can't get over." Her daughter said, "Mom, turn on your signal." So Lisa put on her signal. The very next car let her over, and she exited the freeway.

Use your signals—whether they are lights, words, or actions.

PERSEVERE

One of my main goals in life is to facilitate positive change. I want to build people up, empower them to be their best and open their eyes to the reality of endless possibilities—and to help them find the courage to make the changes that will result in a wonderful life.

I have accomplished many goals in my life that I am proud of: among them graduating from college and losing and keeping off 75 pounds. Both of these goals are things that many other people have accomplished. They are also goals that many people would like to do and haven't. So what is the difference between people who have accomplished the goals and those who haven't? I believe it boils down to one thing: perseverance.

Confucius said, "It doesn't matter how slowly you go as long as you do not stop."

I have nothing inside of me that those people who want to earn a college degree or lose weight don't have. If I can do it, anyone can do it. Decide and then do. Recommit daily to what you want to accomplish. Then redecide that it is still what you want and it is still worth it.

When I explain to people that it took me two years to lose the weight I wanted to lose, they look at me in shock. *Two years?* That's such a long time. I could never have done it that slowly and taken that long. I would think to myself, "I was going to live those two years anyway, so I might as well be able to say that I was happy with my weight at the end of the two years."

Whatever *you* want, it is achievable. One day at a time, one step at a time, one choice at a time.

> *"I have just three things to teach:*
> *Simplicity, patience, compassion.*
> *These three are your greatest treasures."*
> —Lao Tzu

TRUE SUCCESS

What we really want is true success—the kind that happens over time, the kind that lasts. We live in a society that craves immediate gratification, so most people want to accomplish their goals overnight. But anything that happens overnight can be undone overnight.

True success is almost never immediate. It comes only to those who work through the times of frustration and discouragement. True success means choosing to keep going and never give up. No matter what your recipe for success is, perseverance is the main ingredient.

"Great works are performed not by great strength
but by perseverance."
—Samuel Johnson

THIS IS IT!!!

The Five Foundations and the experiences in this book have helped me to develop three of my most valuable tools: self-awareness, self-trust and self-respect. I hope the Five Foundations will have a similar effect on your life.

This is a new moment. Your moment. Be the person you want to be *today*. It is time to look forward, to move in the direction of positive choices and positive change. You can do it. THIS IS IT!

> *"This is my way ... What is your way?*
> *THE WAY doesn't exist."*
> —Friedrich Nietzsche

ISBN 142516550-8